Folktales and Legends of OLD LANCASHIRE

G.M.Dixon

Published by MINIMAX BOOKS

I.S.B.N. 0 906791 73 1
© Minimax Ltd 1991

Printed in England

CONTENTS

THE WINWICK PIG

Winwick, lying between the M6 and Warrington, has a small church dedicated to Saint Oswald. Oswald was the monarch of Northumbria at the time of his death in the year 642. He died in battle against the pagan King Penda of Mercia, and was one of the few kings to be made a saint. The church dedicated to his name was built on the spot where he breathed his last breath.

Once upon a time when England was a land of forest and glade, when the English people were young, and romance and wonder could still be found, Winwick was just a small clearing in the woods. It had no name then, as far as it is known, but there were huts within a palisade and it had a revered place. This was the place where good King Oswald was killed and many were the stories told of this noble and honourable hero. Travellers would call in and pay tribute to the great man, bowing low to the spot and sometimes leaving a token gift. It was almost like a shrine.

The elders of the village cared for it but there was no real guardian of the place. Indeed, all there was was a great stone which had been rolled there to mark the spot. Neither was there a written inscription but the stories were passed on by word of mouth, along with those about Jesus. Christianity had been brought to this country by the Romans, then the stories about it were told by each generation of Anglo-Saxons, along with stories of their own gods, so that the story of Jesus and His good works was kept alive in that way.

By the time of our story, in the early tenth century, Oswald had been dead for many years but his name lived on and his stone was tended. No one knew who placed the stone there or ever questioned its authenticity.

One day the old men of the village sat down under the great tree in the centre of the palisaded area just to talk about things. They watched as a group of noble strangers entered the palisade, walked over to the stone and bowed their heads. The old men looked at each other, seemed to think the same thoughts, and the idea was born of building a church to honour the Saint. There was much more talking, walking around, and then more talking. Many discussions later, it was finally decided that the church was to be built of timber, with stone doorways and windows. No plans were drawn in those days, except for great marks on the ground, but the young men had to know about the proposed new building and what it was to look like. So the old men drew their plans on the ground and showed, in particular, where the doorway was to be. They wanted people to come out of the church and see before them the stone of St Oswald.

Very soon preparations were under way for the building and people were so busy that no-one noticed the old wild boar that entered the palisade and rooted around near the fire to see what he could find.

Stones were gathered together and great trees in the forest were marked in readiness for their felling. The marks on the ground were discussed at great length, adjusted, walked around, and then talked about again. There was great excitement in the village, and all those who came to see the place left something of value which would help finance the construction of the church.

And still the old pig stayed in the palisade, walking around, grunting, snuffling around people, and generally being friendly. Everyone became quite fond of him. He seemed especially interested in the marks on the ground which showed where the new church was to be built, and was often seen there. The men found his rooting around quite amusing but hastened to replace their marks when his grubbing

obliterated them.

It was soon time for the actual building to start and stones were used to mark the corners and doorways of the church, amidst much arm waving and discussion. But, at last the groundwork was done and the men surveyed their work with satisfaction. It was the end of the day and the villagers went home for their evening meal, looking forward to the morrow when they could continue their work.

That night many people in the village heard the old pig rooting and grunting busily but they just smiled and turned over to resume their slumbers.

When the first man awoke the next morning, he left his hut to survey yesterday's work, but soon his loud shout alarmed the whole community. The others came out and stared in amazement at the astonishing scene before them. For, wonderfully, the great stones and the marks which showed the plans of the church had been moved across the square to lie around St Oswald's stone. And strangest of all, there in the middle, seemingly fast asleep, lay the old boar which the villagers had befriended.

The men, women and children moved over to the place, whispering, or talking in low, hushed, almost reverent tones. They saw stones and marks all laid out most accurately and they looked at the wild pig as it lay in the sunshine. They talked of how they had heard the pig at work during the night and eventually drew close to it. Looking at the animal closely they saw that its chest was not rising and falling, and when one man touched it, he sadly pronounced it dead.

The village elders gathered that morning and the talking began again. It was decided that the church would be built exactly as the pig had decreed and that, in memory of the animal, a pig would be carved on the stone that marked the spot where St Oswald had died.

After the church was finished, and as a token of the wonderful event of the moving of the church's foundations, there was built in the churchyard a large wheel cross, carved by the very man who carved the pig on the stone. A part of that wheel cross remains to this day.

Many years later, in the fourteenth century, the church was rebuilt in stone and that very stone, the one on which the pig was carved, was built into the tower. There it has stayed until this day, a token of something deep and mysterious in life.

Just who was the pig? What kind of creature was he? Exactly what link did he have with the old King Oswald? There are those who declare that, after death, our souls are born again into some other creature's body. Who can say that they are wrong? Who has seen through the curtain?

8

THE PENDLE WITCHES

Pendle Hill overlooks some of the most beautiful countryside of Lancashire. Lying in the Ribble Valley, the green and soft hills disclose small villages and hamlets, meadows, fields and copses, woven into a network by byway and stream. And yet explore quietly, in case you awaken some of the spirits of Pendle –the witches who lived there many years ago.

"Look out! Here they come," cried the little boy who had run out of Lancaster with the crowd of other people on the morning of Thursday, August 20th in 1612.

And what a show it promised to be, thought young tousle-haired Dan Latimer, as he stood gazing down the road, his brown eyes sparkling with happy anticipation. There was to be a hanging, and he had never seen one before. But, from what he could understand from others, it was a marvellous thing to watch.

His mother watched him anxiously, not for the first time wondering if it was right to bring the young lad here. In front of her stood a gallows and a troop of the King's Guard who were to supervise the executions. Beside and around her was a laughing, chattering, buzzing crowd of Lancastrians who were out to enjoy themselves. Alice Latimer told her son to come near to her, so that he should not be lost, and together they watched.

They saw a crowd coming along the road and behind them a great wagon drawn by four great black horses. As they came closer, Alice and Dan saw that there were ten bewildered old ladies standing on the cart, guarded by three soldiers armed with pikes. Their grey hair blew in the wind, their black eyes had a lost look in them, their skin was drawn, their clothes were dark: they had been accused of being witches and that was exactly what they looked like. It was a dreadful thing to be accused of in those days for, according to the new laws of King James I, witchcraft was punishable by death.

Now, one by one, they were to be hung by the neck until they were dead. The Reverend Nathaniel Drivett, looking fascinated by the whole event, stepped forward as the cart reached the scaffold and, from the raised platform, asked for God's blessing on the execution, and God's forgiveness on the old ladies. They were not to be forgiven or treated gently by those gathered there on that warm Thursday, though. The guards on the cart roughly thrust forward one of the old women and the rope noose was put around her neck as she stepped on to the platform. To the roar of the crowd, and to the cries of dread from the remaining nine women on the cart, the trapdoor was opened and the first corpse twitched on the end of the rope. The old ladies in the cart screamed and the crowd yelled for more, but Alice Latimer, horrified, had taken the shaking Dan in her arms and carried him away from the ghastly sight.

It had all begun less than six short months before. Alizon Demdike had been begging near Colne and when the pedlar, John Law, passed by, she asked him for some pins. His living was poor, so he refused and the beggar cursed him for his meanness. He looked at her and she stared back hard. As John Law turned away and eye contact was broken, he suffered a stroke and suddenly fell down to the ground. Both he and Alizon attributed this to the curse, but she laughed alone, loudly and harshly.

John Law's condition deteriorated over the next few days and he complained to the local guard. They arrested Alizon and tried her, with John Law as the chief witness. The Clerk of the Court recorded that John Law was in a poor condition by then: "his hede was drawne awrie, his eeyes and face deformed, his speche not wele to bee underestode, and his legges starcke lame".

The local magistrate, Roger Nowell, questioned Alizon and what a tale sprang from her lips. She told tales of her wild, squint-eyed mother, Bessie Demdike, her blind grandmother, eighty-year-old Mother Demdike and her half-wit brother, James. She told how her grandmother had visited Richard Baldwin, the miller at Wheathead, to beg some money from him. He refused and told her to go away and had been cursed soundly in return. "Go and hang yourself," she shouted to the miller. A year later the miller's daughter died and old Mother Demdike told Alizon that she had bewitched the child.

Roger Nowell gathered together the others who Alizon implicated and asked them questions. Strangely, no torture was used to induce confessions and it seemed odd that these

11

people willingly and voluntarily practically convicted themselves. Strange, that is, even when one realises that the chief witness against the witches was old Mother Demdike's grand-daughter, the nine year old Jennet. Old Chattox, another beggar woman, half crazy, half blind, withered and decrepit, was involved, together with another six, until there were eleven self-confessed witches. The strangest of these was a relatively wealthy woman who was happily married, Alice Nutter, who lived at Roughlee Hall and enjoyed a comfortable life.

However, Magistrate Nowell could satisfy the law that the eleven women had talked, planned and acted with imps and the Devil, had dug up graves, plotted with the Devil to blow up Lancaster Castle and had been involved in the deaths of sixteen people in the neighbourhood. They were convicted of practising black magic and sentenced to meet the end that the law said was appropriate: death at the end of a rope. Until that could be arranged the eleven were incarcerated within Lancaster Castle, and it was there that old Mother Demdike died peacefully, leaving the remaining ten to suffer the pain and humiliation of a public hanging. Perhaps her last spell was the most powerful of all, and cast upon herself?

In the apparent peacefulness of present day Pendle, it all seems very strange, but perhaps there was more to it than the oft portrayed catching of eleven duped simpletons. Could it be that the eleven women were proud of their witchcraft? Perhaps there was something evil amongst the villages and hamlets of Pendle. Perhaps there still is.

Pendle Hill

THE FOOTPRINT BURNT IN STONE

Bolton, a town famed in the cotton industry as the home of Samuel Crompton, is an interesting place to visit. It is set amidst green countryside where both the unexpected and the grotesque can be found. For instance, Smithills Hall, about two miles north-west of Bolton, is one of the oldest half-timbered manor houses in Lancashire. It was built in the 14th Century and extended in Tudor times. Smithills is open to the public – pay a visit, walk through its passageways and rooms and a grisly sight will be found.

The reign of Mary I (1553-1558) was an unhappy and cruel five year interlude in the history of Great Britain. Mary became queen after the death of her fifteen-year-old half brother, Edward, who was the son of Henry VIII and his beloved wife, Jane Seymour. Mary, the daughter of Henry and the Catholic Catherine of Aragon, was determined to restore Britain to the church of her mother, the Catholic church of Rome which Henry had broken away from. Mary was a bitter woman, and was responsible for many cruel deeds, mainly in the name of religion. One of the first things she did after her coronation was order the execution of a number of important men, including the Duke of Northumberland. Then she forbade the people to say their prayers or read the bible in English and, because Catholic clergymen were not allowed to marry, the clergy were ordered to send away their wives.

We can read in our history books of the Protestant martyrs who died during this time because of their reformed beliefs. Men such as Bishop Latimer, Bishop Ridley and Archbishop Cranmer and many, many others died in very cruel circumstances, often by being burnt alive. Over in Spain at the

13

same time the Spanish Inquisition was going on and people were dying even more horrendous deaths, also in the name of religion. It was a Prince of Spain, later to become King Philip of Spain, who Mary chose to marry, and for this the English people never forgave her. She died in 1558, a lonely and hated woman, who was responsible for the doing of many evil deeds.

At Smithills Hall, near Bolton in Lancashire, there is real evidence of that evil.

George Marsh was the vicar of the local church and he was much revered in his parish. His services were the new English language ones that King Henry VIII had introduced so that the people could understand and follow the prayers. For nearly eighteen years these services had been used and George Marsh was pleased that the people seemed to respond well to them. Much good work had been done in the village and the vicar believed that it was because the people were now closer to their God. James I was yet to come, with his Authorised Version of the Bible and the prayer book, but the groundwork had been laid. George, and many others like him, were proud of the good work that the Protestants had done in bringing about the Church of England. He resented the Roman Church and all that it stood for and had been keen to help with the building of the new one. He lived for the Church of England and, if necessary, he was prepared to die for it.

When news first came to Lancashire about Queen Mary's intention to restore the Church of Rome, George Marsh told his friends that he would never weaken his principles. He was used to the weak ways of King Henry and King Edward and did not believe that he would have to alter his thinking. "I believe in what I am doing," he said. "Do you think I would practise what I did not preach?" It seemed to be a simple enough thing to say. There was no-one there to contradict, oppose or to threaten him. Sitting there at the dinner table, surrounded by friends, happy in his work, it was difficult to believe that anyone would take any notice of what he said. In that forgotten corner of Lancashire, Queen Mary and London seemed far away.

Later on though, when news filtered through of cruel treatment and persecution of those who followed their Protestant beliefs, a cold shiver went down his spine. What if ..... ? George Marsh, gentle and courteous man that he was, could not conceive of such deeds in reality and breathed easily once more. He smiled and carried on with his English services, even after he was warned that this just would not do. "I am George Marsh," he thought, "with a commission from God to minister to these people. My life, my work, my life's work is built upon the belief that people must understand their God. And I will not desist. No. Never."

One Sunday, when he was in the middle of his service in church, they came for him: dark clothed men with shaded faces. Dark men, silent men, who silently led him off to Smithills Hall.

They led him to a darkened room where he waited for three whole days with little to sustain him but bread and water. He sat there, deep in thought, or prayed devoutly on his knees, reflecting deeply and confirming his beliefs time and time again.

One morning these dark clothed men came for him again, taking him this time to the Green Room, which can still be seen today. There, a long table was arranged, bare and highly polished, with eight chairs behind it. On those chairs sat solemn men, quiet men, dressed in black with black jowls and dark features. For eight solid hours they questioned him: asked him the same questions in different ways, over and over again. They hoped that he would change his mind and his ways. George Marsh hoped that they could accept that he would not. It was a useless eight hours, and agreement was impossible.

"You will burn in hell," said the man in the centre. "You stand condemned by your own words. You preach a false doctrine."

"If I am to burn in hell, then I am burning now, for heaven and hell truly begin in this life," replied George Marsh fervently.

"By his own words," said one of the dark men. "From his own lips," said another. "He has condemned himself," and "What more is there to say?" The inquisitors were united: "He has said it all."

The leader of the Queen's men said, "We sentence you to be burnt."

George Marsh simply replied, "I burn now."

"What heresy is this: to say that you burn now?" Mr Marsh simply bowed his head.

"Take him from here to Boughton in Cheshire where he will be burnt. Now take him from here; see if he burns now."

The guardians stood and led him out, through the door and into the passage.

"You burn? Burn now, you heretic," said the leader of the court.

George Marsh turned, smiled and a powerful glow surrounded him. The guardians fell backwards, shocked. Those behind the table turned, stunned, as George Marsh glowed with a divine radiance. Then he smiled and the glow died. The guardians stood again and led him on, silent as when they first arrived. But those behind the table stared at the floor where George Marsh had stood. A footprint had been burned into the very stone.

16

That footprint can be seen today, just outside the Green Room.
A footprint burnt into the stone.

JENNY GREENTEETH

Clitheroe, a beautiful little Lancashire town, nestles quietly in a fairytale valley of the River Ribble. Just outside Clitheroe where the road to Waddington crosses it, that river sweeps broadly, in smooth expanses just right for the fisherman. But, beware, for old Jenny Greenteeth is there, somewhere!

Beware as you walk the path by the River Ribble, my dears. Do not be misled by the sunshine, or by the light breeze. Do not be deceived by the singing of the birds. Believe me, readers, that sunshine will lose its warmth, the breeze will grow chill and the birds will suddenly be struck dumb. Evil is there by that river, an evil, once aroused, from which no human can escape. It is not by chance that, once every seven years, some hapless stranger loses his life, dragged to a watery grave, never to be seen again.

Now, I can guess that you are curious. You want to know how it happens. Well, if you sit comfortably, you can take the time to hear the tale.

Once upon a time, so I have been told, there was an old woman called Jenny Greenteeth who lived in a little tumble-down cottage not far from the bank of the River Ribble. It was there, where the trees and bushes grow thickly, for those clay walls and thatched roof have once more joined the earth from which they grew. Old Jenny fed upon the berries and fruits of the woods, the harvest of the hedgerows and the wild creatures that she caught. At the end of her garden was a well, and it was from there that she drew the crystal clear water that she drank.

Life should have been full of happiness, for Jenny lived in a woodland wonderland of bright flowers, green leaves and shafts of golden sunshine, a delight of scents and a richness of tastes. The magic of Spring, the fairyland of Summer, the kaleidoscope of Autumn and the stillness of Winter were all there to spread radiance and glory into her life. But it did not work that way, for the waspish Jenny Greenteeth did not want to be happy.

When she was a young maid, Jenny had been crossed in love by a young man of the village and she fled to the woods then, in self-pity and anger. Her once striking beauty soon vanished and, as she aged, she turned into a pinched, snivelling cross-patch. Her life was devoted to stealing beauty, beauty that was once hers. She stole the beauty of the violet hiding beneath the tree stumps by stamping on it; she ransacked the birds' nests; she robbed the blackberry bushes of their jewelled fruit and threw them upon the ground; she plundered the mushrooms in the meadows by taking a few and rubbing the rest into the ground with her foot; she stripped the berries from the mountain ash in case they should feed the starving winter birds. She despoiled the woods in which she lived: a veritable hag, and the bane of all around her.

The once beautiful woodland suffered silently at the hands of Jenny Greenteeth, only lamenting when the breezes of Spring moaned through the branches, only crying when the twigs dripped in the Autumn, the great tears dropping unhindered to the ground. Then it was that Jenny Greenteeth cackled with laughter at the hideous torment that she had caused.

But Mother Nature cares, my dears, and although revenge is sometimes a long time coming, she always sets things right in the end.

One day, Jenny Greenteeth went to draw a pail of water from her well. It was one of those Autumn days when the tears had been falling from the trees as they seemed to express their sorrow. Jenny threw the pail into the well and leaned over to watch it. The bucket filled with water and Jenny, in her great skirts and with her shawl over her head, leaned forward more and started to pull the rope in order to get the bucket of water. But her smooth-soled boots slipped on the wet pathway and she over-balanced, falling into the well! Still holding on to the

rope, Jenny hurtled down the shaft, screaming as she fell. As she hit the water, the rope pulled tight, the bucket caught in the wheel above the well and water from the bucket rained on the old harridan's head!

What a fine mess for old Jenny Greenteeth to be in – ugly and awful, but quite deserved. She was cold, wet and her cries for help floated up out of the well so very faintly. No-one could hear the plaintive screams that arose, and Jenny was unable to help herself. She tried to haul herself up, but the weight of her clothes, and her increasingly chilled body, soon left her helpless.

Yes, my dears, she died, drowned in that well, but her soul would not rest. Sometimes her spirit takes on the form of a green bush near the river, sometimes a flower by the weir, sometimes a clump of reeds: always one of the growing things that she maltreated. It bides its time, waiting for the right moment, looking for its chance. Once every seven years it springs into action, and someone disappears. So do stay away from the river edge after dark, my dears. Hurry home and be glad that you are safe, for old Jenny Greenteeth might have had you if you had been careless.

TROUBLE AT MILL

Lancashire today is vastly different to the county in the last century. In those not so long ago days the cotton towns were famous throughout the world. Pictures of factories, stories of working in them, and life in those hard times were the inspiration for books of all kinds. If you want to know what life was like then, visit the Queen Street Mill in Burnley. Listen to the noise and see the sights but, if you don't want to be depressed, try not to imagine too closely life as it was.

Joseph, Joe to his friends, lay in the sweet smelling grass on the bank of the road leading to Worsthorne, revelling in the sunshine. Looking down the road he could see the tall chimneys of the factories with their grey smoke rising high over the green hills. Birds sang but he could hear the hum from Burnley above them; Joe put his head in the grass and despaired. He thought of his mother and father and of his eight brothers and sisters. They would be worried about him. Last night had been a long one and he was very hungry now, after twenty-four hours without food. His stomach was so empty that he felt ill with hunger and chewed some grass, but this made him feel worse.

It was 1834 and although Joe was only eleven years old he had already been at work in Queen Street Mill for three years. Joe thought of yesterday and his heart lurched. He dared not think of tomorrow and the uncertainty and fear that it contained. As he thought of the day before, the events came vividly back to his mind.

Joe woke up in his family's little tenement in Mill Street as usual. He had been awoken by his older brother, his two elder sisters and his parents as they arose. Then the five younger children woke up and two began to cry. The children were all in the same bed and their room was only separated from their parents' room by a thin lathe wall. No-one washed and, in the gloom of the single guttering candle, they ate rough rye bread, and drank water from a bucket. The walls were black with damp and the fire burnt more to cook than to warm or dry the house. Stools, chairs and a bare table were the only furnishing on a bare brick floor which was cold, hard and dusty. Joe looked at his parents, both face down, cheerlessly chewing their bread, and at his brothers and sisters, also eating their poor food. Their hair was tousled, matted and infested with lice. The clothes they wore were thin and dirty and their feet were bare. There were just three pairs of clogs in the house. Joe's bright eyes looked round and filled with tears at the hopelessness of it all. He wondered what life could possibly hold for him.

Then the footsteps in the street started and mother, father and the four eldest children went out, leaving the five young ones alone to fend for themselves all day. Along the narrow unlit streets and alleys they tramped, with their friends and neighbours, towards Queen Street Mill. As they passed the great open gate, the gaslight from the factory windows threw a yellow glare that was almost dazzling to the poor people from their dark homes. The family separated, each child going off to his or her own place of work and the parents taking their places at the great spinning mules. There were hundreds of children working there, many at the machines, but some in the warehouses and packing rooms. Some of them were given little tins of oil with which to keep the machinery oiled, others were placed at various points along the machines so that if anything should happen to stop the machine, they would crawl in and sort out the tangle or the break in the thread. Some children had brushes and dustpans and their jobs were to keep the machines and floors clean. Still others had to fetch and carry the reels, bobbins and tapes needed to keep the great machines humming and grinding.

Joe was a 'scavenger' and it was his job to use his dustpan and brush to keep the machines and floor in his section clear of the dust that the cotton made. The thin lines of sunlight slanting through the windows showed up this dust and soon Joe and the other workers would be coughing and spluttering as the dust got into their lungs. Joe had a friend called Bobby who was also a 'scavenger'. "Poor little Bobby," thought Joe, as he looked at the puny body that already had that stooped look of an old man. A year ago Bobby caught his hand in the spinning machine and Joe could remember his screams, even now, as two little boys dragged him away, blood pouring from his hand. Of course, the machine could not be stopped – uneconomical. Bobby lost four fingers from his left hand but received not a penny of compensation, just the reputation for being an irresponsible little boy. He was told to consider himself lucky that the mill manager had him taken home. The screams of poor Bobby still rang in the whirring machinery for Joe and he had often woken up screaming after a nightmare, only to be kicked and cursed by his brothers for waking them. And so Joe listened to the machines and he worried.

The Lancashire voices of the men, women and children laughed, sang and cursed in that mill room and Joe worked through it, in a dream-world of his own, miles away. Suddenly a scream curdled his blood and echoing cries made him stand away from under the machine. He saw that Hannah, a neighbour and a girl of his own age, had put her head too close to one of the big driving belts. The buckle had caught in her long hair, swung her up to the ceiling and there she was suspended, screaming awfully over the pulley.

"Stop the machine," yelled Joe, but to no avail.

A quick thinking youth balanced precariously on a machine, a large knife in his hand. With one swipe, he cut Hannah's hair and then, holding the child, fell to the ground, dangerously near a spinning machine.

Joe did not stop to think; he threw down his brush and pan and rushed out of the factory. Through the streets and roads he ran, not looking, not caring where he went. Out of the dim streets and into the countryside of lanes, hedges, trees and birds. Hours later, exhausted, Joe fell down by a stream and sobbed until it seemed as if his heart would break. He sobbed, alone and unseen, until he fell into a deep, deep sleep.

Now here he was, the next morning, hungry, alone and sad. So sad and sick of this world. A man came along and looked at him, then Joe was suddenly afraid of being alone. He rose to his feet, straightened his back, and resolutely walked back through the roads and the streets again until, late that afternoon, he came to Queen Street Mill once more. What other choice did he have? He walked through the gate and found Mr. Blincoe, the supervisor for his room, and said that he had been ill. "Alright, lad, now go back to your machine," Mr. Blincoe said, understanding a little of what had happened, "but just go first and see your mam and dad."

Joe did just that, his tear stained face telling his parents all that they wished to know. Then back to his machine he went, an older and wiser boy.

Eventually Joe became a supervisor himself and took Hannah as his wife. They had four fine children, three boys and a girl, but all this was in the future as far as our story is concerned. Eight years later, Joe's head was just one of thousands that nodded in agreement when child labour was finally abolished.

THE CHILDE OF HALE

Hale lies about five miles to the east of Liverpool and was once thought to be one of the prettiest villages in England. It is still an attractive place today, with its little cottages, pleasant flower gardens and old church. In the yard of the 15th Century church lies a grave – a grave with a story.

One fine day in the year 1578, a boy was born in the village of Hale and given the name of John. His mother and father, Sarah and Elia Hale, were ordinary people and John grew up in the cottage along with his brothers and sisters.

His boyhood whittled away happily, no school in those days to oppress the young. Everything they knew was learned at home or in the village, and life was simple then. John used to spend time helping his parents, often weeding between the vegetables or chopping wood. His mind often seemed to be on other things though, and his mother regularly saw him looking off into the distance and day-dreaming. "Fair mizzled, he is," she declared, but John's father thought that he might have a yearning for the sea, as he was always gazing off in that direction.

One day, when John was thirteen, he suddenly announced, "I want to go to see the great ocean. I feel that I have got to go to the shore for a certain reason, I know not what."

His mother was very worried, without really knowing why, but she did not want to spoil her son's day, and waved goodbye to him smilingly along with the rest of the family.

The coast was only about six miles away from Hale, just to the south of where Liverpool stands now, and the sun shone down on John as he strode out with his lunch in a pack on his back.

He met travellers on his way, some of them men of the sea, but John was quite shy and spoke to no-one on his two hour walk to the great Atlantic Ocean.

When he arrived he looked in awe at the golden sands stretching out to the horizon and at the quiet and lonely dunes. John walked on to the sand and gazed at the great waves which crashed on the shore. He walked along the strand and then back to where he had started. Sitting on the beach, he undid his pack and ate the lunch that his mother had prepared. The sun shone warmly on his back and when he had finished eating, he lay back on the sand and soon was fast asleep.

Now, what happened next was open to speculation. Some say that a creature from the sea crawled from the water and lay near him. Others say that a shaft of sunlight from the sea affected him. It has also been said that an evil person's curse, someone from his family's past, was put upon him. Mostly it was said that an old witch from the dunes, jealous of his youth and strength, bewitched him.

Whatever the cause, what is certain was the difference in John when he awoke. During the short sleep he had grown from his five feet two inches in height to well over six feet. His clothes were torn where he had grown, and it was a frightened, confused, and sad looking lad who crept back home later that night. Of course his parents, and indeed the whole family, were also confused and frightened, even frightened of John in case he brought the evil home with him.

A few days were sufficient to show that he was not changed in any other way, and was quite harmless, but each day he seemed to grow a little higher. His mother was kept busy making new clothes for him, ever bewailing the expense, yet not too loud for she did not want to drive him away. Neighbours laughed at him, but never to his face for John was both large and strong. He grew and grew until by the time he was twenty he was nine feet, three inches tall.

His fame spread far and wide and he was even called to London so that King James I could see John for himself. John was a gentle creature, but people often tempted him to prove his strength. When he was at the court of King James, the King himself ordered John to fight the court wrestler. John had no appetite for the fight, and neither did the court wrestler when he saw the size of his opponent! However, loyal to the King, the wrestler jumped at John, who simply seized his thumb, bent it back effortlessly, and it broke. This action caused John to lose favour with the King and he was sent home in disgrace. On his way home, a bull attacked him, head down and roaring dreadfully. John just stood his ground and when the bull met

him, John seized its horns, turned, and threw the bull completely over the hedge. There it stood, confused and thoroughly out of sorts, staring at John until he disappeared over the horizon.

The Childe of Hale, for so John became known, lived quietly in his home village for the rest of his life, working steadily on a farm where his strength was very useful.

Later in his life, John became ill with the fever and was bedridden for some time. His huge bed had been moved downstairs for safety's sake, and even so his parents were afraid he would fall from his bed and hurt himself when the fever wracked him badly. To save him from this they obtained a great chain and used it to fasten him into his bed. When John recovered, the chain was revered for its proven strength and so was divided into three pieces and each piece used for some important purpose. One was taken to Chester to keep the mills from floating from the Dee and into the sea; another was sent to Lincolnshire where it tethered the tower of St Botolph's Church, the well-known Boston Stump, so that it would not be blown out to sea. The third piece of chain went off to the nether world where it was used to fetter the Devil who had been captured whilst suffering from stomach ache.

This was the last tale that was ever heard of the Childe of Hale, John Middleton, who died when he was forty-five years old. He lies peacefully in the shaded churchyard at Hale, quiet and still, his resting place marked by the great tombstone which is still well-tended to this day.

BACUP DANCERS

At the south end of the Forest of Rossendale lies the little town of Bacup. Quiet and seemingly featureless, Bacup has some really interesting traditions, old and new. Visit the Wall of History in Newgate Garden at the bottom of Todmorden Road, it is well worth while. What Bacup is known best for, though, are the Britannia Coco-nut Dancers.

On Easter Saturday each year the Britannia Coco-nut Dancers gambol the seven miles from one side of Bacup to the other, watched and enjoyed by thousands of people.

The troupe has eight members and they enjoy donning their traditional, and yet exotic, costumes to amuse the public. Their faces are blackened and the basic costume of black polo necked sweater and velvet knee breeches are decorated with red piping. Then there are the red and blue ribands, red and blue pom-poms, the rosettes and the white hats with blue feathers – apart from the leader who has a red feather in his. Short white skirts with shoulder straps are worn over the breeches, each decorated by three red hoops. White socks and black clogs complete the outfits, apart from the belt, that is, which is hung with wooden discs to match the ones hanging around the dancers' knees. The troupe perform seven dances, five garland dances and two nut dances, 'Thowd Crash' and 'The Figures'. These last two are unique to the Bacup Dancers and they are performed using the wooden discs hanging from their costumes, along with others which are hand-held. These discs, when struck together, make rippling and accompanying rhythms, just as sticks are used in other parts of the country. The music is provided by a concertina usually but, on larger occasions like the Easter parades, an eight piece brass band is used.

Through the streets go the dancers, eagerly watched and applauded, they have many followers and there is never a shortage of men wanting to join their ranks. Join the spectators on Easter Saturday, share in the gaiety and the revelry. Close your eyes for a moment, slip back through time and wonder about where it all began.

Long, long ago, when Cornwall was the eastern fringe of the great lost continent of Atlantis, gods were traditionally worshipped in ceremonies which were vital to the occult meaning of life. After the destruction of the Kingdom of Atlantis, the world changed as people from the borders of the lost continent began to travel and to explore. But some traditions continued and, at a certain time of the year, men danced in patterns which had come from the lost generations. They wove the ancient steps and performed rituals which had previously been connected with the fertilisation of all living things. For centuries the tradition of the ancient dance was continued, for what disaster would befall them if they forgot?

On the 24th of June, 1340, England won the great naval battle at Sluys, and so began twenty years of total command of the seas in all the known world. People came to England from many countries to trade, and with this trade came the pirates. Dark skinned men from North Africa especially came to this country, having reaped a rich harvest from the fat merchant ships in the English Channel. Cornwall became a favourite port of call and many a wedding followed the landing of ships. The Moors from North Africa saw the ancient dances being performed and joined in, adding their own traditional steps, music and costumes to the ancient Cornish ones. Years passed and, through the centuries, the ancient dances were performed as by the Moors, so becoming known as Moorish ...... Morris ...... dancing.

In the late 1700's tin mining was one of the main occupations in Cornwall, but the niggardly and tightfisted owners of the mines made life very difficult for the men who mined the rich seams. Their families were large, their cottages small and money and food were scarce, but the Cornish men still knew how to enjoy themselves. Spare time was spent bowling, drinking, gardening and dancing – Morris Dancing. These men were generally big and strong but were skilful and lively dancers in spite of this, for they had performed since they were very young. Easter Saturday was the big day in the dancers' calendar, the day when they were on show for seemingly the whole of Cornwall.

Two of the leading members of a Southern Cornish dancing troupe were Ted Finch and Tom Barnes, both tin miners who were very disgruntled by their working conditions and pay. One day they were in conversation with a traveller, a man from the north who was there to find out about the mining industry in Cornwall. He told them of the mines being opened up in Lancashire and the need for skilled miners who could bring coal from mine shafts and quarries. This man, Samuel Duffield, made life in Lancashire sound very attractive indeed and, within a month, Tom and Ted, along with their families and others, found themselves on the road to the Forest of Rossendale. They did not have many possessions and must have looked a sorry sight as they arrived at Whitworth – but they soon cheered up as they were able to move straight into cottages which had just been freshly built. The men of Cornwall soon settled into their new homes and jobs, but did not forget their traditions.

The following Spring the urge to dance was upon them and within a short time they had organised a troupe of men and the dancing began again. Their faces were blackened with burnt cork and with their fancy clothes and curious steps, they soon attracted a crowd of spectators who wanted to join them. Morris dancing became very popular and a number of troupes evolved. It was from one of these, the Tunstead Mill Troupe, that the Britannia group sprang.

And so the tradition of Morris dancing, and whatever came before it, continues, and long may it do so, especially in the form of the Britannia Coco-nut Dancing Troupe of Bacup.

THE MIRACULOUS BABY OF LATHOM

Lathom Park, now belonging to the Pilkington Glass Company, has a ruin in its centre. It is a ruin of an old hall, romantic in its dereliction. Grey and lone it stands on a grassy mound rising from the old drive. Empty windows, there are, and on the shattered plaster above the door can be seen the decayed remains of the family crest: an eagle, and a clue to a fascinating story.

It was long ago, in the days of King Edward III, that this story took place. They were dark days indeed, for during this reign the Hundred Years War with France began, and as if that was not bad enough, in 1346 the Black Death swept the country. In Lancashire the effects of these events were sorely felt. Sons, husbands and fathers were called away to fight for their country; young lives and good health bled away on the fields of France, and for what? Even more dreaded, though, was the death-carrying pestilence which crept unseen into homes to wreak indiscriminate havoc and tragedy.

At his home, Lathom Hall, Sir Thomas Lathom worried about the suffering of the people in his neighbourhood. "Poor, poor people," said Sir Thomas to his wife, Evelyn, as they sat by the fire in the great hall. "I wish that there was something that we could do for them."

Lady Evelyn watched him as he sat fiddling with his collar and lapels. "Do you dear?" she asked, maintaining her customary neutral composure. They were both approaching thirty-five years of age and although they had one daughter, Isabella, a son had so far eluded them. Perhaps more than anything Sir Thomas yearned for an heir to succeed him to his title and the great estate that surrounded the hall.

"I think that I will go down into the village tomorrow to see if there is anything that I can do," mused Sir Thomas, then nodded as his wife asked him to be careful.

And so it was that next morning, cutting a fine figure on his black horse, Sir Thomas rode down to the village. He was accompanied by his steward, John Burrows, and the two of them found much suffering. The steward took notes of the plight of the villagers and of what was needed to help them. Soon, blankets were being delivered, food was provided, two roofs were repaired, a wall was mended and a blacksmith was sent to see to the foot of a lame horse. John Burrows was kept very busy and sometimes he was accompanied by his master, for Sir Thomas's roving eye had caught sight of Mary Oskatell, the daughter of a soldier lost in France. Whilst John Burrows was with the Widow Oskatell writing details of the gable to be repaired, Sir Thomas was lightly chatting with Mary. He found out that she went to wash her clothes in the stream every Monday morning and that she was without a suitor. She in turn found the handsome nobleman attractive, perhaps because of his maturity, or perhaps because of his money.

Not by chance was Sir Thomas riding by the stream the next Monday morning. It was a lovely May morning, the birds were singing their loudest and sweetest, and every bough was hung with verdant green leaves and heavily scented blossom. Even the grass held a softness and perfume, as Sir Thomas and Mary found out as they bathed in the sunshine of their love.

Perhaps it was the stolen nature of their love that made it so exciting for the couple, but as the summer progressed, and they saw each other daily, their fond feelings grew and grew.

Lady Evelyn walked through the lawned grounds of the hall with her daughter Isabella, and as the child chattered, the mother became more thoughtful. She knew exactly what was

35

going on, she thought: her husband was involving himself more and more in the lives of the villagers, helping them with their grief as death and illness struck at their homes. It was born out of a desire to do good, thought Lady Evelyn, never suspecting for a moment that her husband was indulging himself in a dalliance.

Along came winter and Sir Thomas became very worried because his lover was now heavy with child. As the day of its birth drew closer, he wondered more and more about how he could explain the birth of the child to his wife. Almost in desperation, he turned to an old lady who used to work in the hall when he was a boy, and it was she who suggested the solution.

One morning, late in February, when the Lady Evelyn and her daughter were out for their daily walk, they heard the cry of a child coming from the base of a great tree wherein an eagle nested. Approaching the tree, Evelyn saw a cot, and in it, a baby who was crying lustily. She gathered it up in her arms, warming and comforting the child as she did so, and carried it indoors, looking for her husband. Lady Evelyn quickly explained what had happened and she and Sir Thomas decided to bring up the child as if he were their own.

This was a very satisfactory arrangement for all concerned, even for Mary as she was brought into the hall to be the baby's nursemaid. He was named Oskatell and was brought up as the son of the family, a brother to Isabella, and Sir Thomas made both children joint heirs to the family fortunes.

It was Oskatell who took the eagle crest for his own emblem, as the front of the old hall still discloses. The strange twist to this story is that Isabella, in time, married Captain Stanley of the

House of the Earls of Derby. They too have an eagle and child on their crest!

THE DEVIL'S BRIDGE

The beautiful little town of Kirkby Lonsdale lies in the far north of Lancashire. Stand in the gateway to the Norman church of St Mary's and look out over the gorgeously unspoilt Lune Valley; the view is absolutely entrancing. Then take the stone steps down to the river and walk the half mile to the deep dark pool of salmon, overhung by Devil's Bridge. Allow the beguiling charm of legend to take you into its embrace.

There was a storm coming up over Castleton Fell, the great black clouds making the morning gloomy and forbidding. It was one of those October days when the countryside showed all its sturdy character in a slow silence. Dolly Brooker, though, was far from silent and absolutely furious. She had woken up that morning knowing that there was a great deal to do and not a minute to waste. In her little cottage on the outskirts of Kirkby all was neat and shining, and so it should be with her daughter coming to visit her that afternoon. She had swept and dusted all through her little living room and a bright fire crackled in the hearth. Cups were arranged on the table and, before the fire, a bowl of kneaded dough lay to rise beneath its covering cloth. The scent of the yeast in the dough spread throughout the house and old Dolly looked and sniffed appreciatively. There would be little for Laurie, her daughter, to grumble about.

Dolly took the milking pail from its hook by the kitchen door, put two buns into her pocket to entice the cow, and left the house. She went to the piece of grass across the road where Betsy the cow was tethered. The milking could be done while the dough was rising, then the milk could cool on the stone kitchen floor ready for Laurie's visit. Sniff, her great brown and black dog, scampered up to her as she went down the path and nearly knocked the pail from her grasp. "You dog of Satan,"

snapped Dolly. "Can't you be more careful?" Sniff did not seem to mind Dolly's chiding tones and bounded through the gate at the end of the path. Dolly followed him out and walked into the road then came to a sudden halt, all thoughts of the dog gone from her mind. The cow, which usually stood looking at her with great brown eyes .... The rope and log to which it was always tied lay on the ground, but the cow was gone!

Dolly threw down her pail and, calling to Sniff, she swung off down the road just hoping that she was going the right way. The wind was chilly and it tugged at the shawl that Dolly pulled tightly round her shoulders. Her grey hair fell across her face as she looked right and left, hoping for sight or sound of her cow. Sniff barked with delight at this new adventure; the wind excited him so that he dashed backwards and forwards as he joined in the quest.

Soon they came to the River Lune which gurgled and streamed round the rocks in its path. Its white and grey waters had been fed by the recent rains and Sniff ventured to its banks and stood there with one foot raised. Dolly shook her head and said, "Come, Sniff." But Sniff still stood there and barked so that Dolly stopped and dragged her straggling hair from her eyes. "Drat it!" she said, as she saw what Sniff had been trying to point out to her. Her cow was beyond a great pool in the river. It was the pool where youngsters sported in the hot summer weather, for it was always deep and cool. Now it was cold and its depth was dangerous, so Dolly stamped her foot with impatience as she thought of the long walk she would have to take to fetch the silly animal. Betsy looked over at her mistress with such innocent deep brown eyes, seeming pleased to see her.

Dolly sat down on a rock and bowed her head in her hands, with Sniff whining anxiously at her ankles. Suddenly she felt very, very dizzy and strange and, as she opened her eyes, the whole world seemed to whirl around her. Then it was still, thank goodness, and she stood, ready for the long walk to fetch the cow. However, from behind the rock that she had been sitting on came a strange dark figure, the very sight of which caused poor old Dolly almost to turn to stone! She felt herself go ice cold inside and her hair stood on end. Sniff whimpered and cringed as the figure drew near.

A crack appeared in the ghastly face of the creature as it stood with hooded slitted eyes, looking at her. A dark cloak covered its body and head and it moved with a kind of creeping, lurching motion that was chillingly evil. "Would you like a bridge to cross the pool, old lady?" croaked the voice entombed in slime.

"Yes," answered Dolly as if in a trance.

"Well, you will have one, and I will have the soul of the first living creature to cross it, even if it be yours."

"Indeed, yes," quavered Dolly.

Immediately, the storm over Castleton Fell broke with a fury of screaming wind, forked lightening and bulleting hail so that Dolly fell behind the sheltering rock. She lay there, rivetted with fear, her shawl pulled tightly over her head and shoulders and Sniff, terrified, pushed himself in to the shelter of her body. The skies opened and the storm beat down, down on the earth and rocks which seemed to move with such crashing and grinding sounds that Dolly thought the world itself was at an end. Eventually, after what seemed an eternity, all was still and with a tranquillity that hurt her ears after the pandemonium of the tempest.

Dolly lifted her head and gasped at what she saw. There above the pool stood a fine new bridge, each stone neatly set in place as if by skilled and wise craftsmen, and built so well that it seemed as though it would last as long as life on earth. Beneath the bridge lay a welter of rocks and stones which the Devil, for surely it must have been he, had cast aside as he searched for those sufficiently perfect for the task. Dolly stood up, and Sniff was once more renewed to his former high spirits. A shy sun peeped out from behind the clouds and a gentle breeze swept the hurricane from her mind. On the other side of the pool Betsy the cow stood looking at her with lost brown eyes, ready to go home for milking. Dolly climbed the bank but before she stepped on to the bridge she remembered the words of Satan, "..... I will have the soul of the first living creature to cross it."

On a sudden impulse, the old lady took a bun from her apron pocket and threw it as hard as she could across the bridge, with Sniff in hot pursuit. Between the parapets he raced, reached the bun, sniffed it and ate it. He looked back at Dolly once, just the once, before a mad light came into his eyes and he raced off across the moors, never to be seen again. As Sniff disappeared, Dolly felt a blast of wind and heard an angry howl of frustration as Satan saw what had happened. His rage was so great that he leapt from the bridge and, as he leapt, Dolly saw that his red hot foot left an imprint. She smiled grimly and quietly said, "Do you think my soul is so cheap that I would throw it away just like that?"

She fetched her cow, the bridge now free from its evil, and went on her way, leaving us all a bridge to wonderland, a bridge that can still be safely crossed today. There, too, for all to see, is that mark of Satan's footprint, still etched on the stone, a testament to the fact that our souls are never so cheap that we can throw them away for any earthly pleasure or ease.

EMMELINE PANKHURST

"Votes for Women" was the cry not so very long ago. Votes for all men and women is something which we take for granted now but it was once a burning issue for many. A tablet on the Free Trade Hall in Manchester helps us to remember a brave lady who devoted her life, successfully, to "Votes for Women".

On July 4th 1858, Emmeline Pankhurst was born in Manchester, the eldest daughter of Sophia Jane Craine and her husband, Robert Goulden. She was the third of eleven children, all of whom were brought up in an atmosphere of wealth and compassion.

Both of Emmeline's parents were wealthy, but they were not the sort of people to enjoy their privileges and forget about the welfare of the people who worked for them in their calico printing factory and the bleach works. The Goulden's were enthusiastic supporters of many things but Mrs Goulden was particularly keen on rights for women. She believed that women should be able to vote, or have the suffrage, as it was then known. People who felt this way were known as suffragettes and, after attending her first meeting at fourteen, Emmeline became one of them. It could never have been foretold then that she would become so famous, a heroine even, in the future. In her own heyday she was considered by the fashionable to be an undesirable, especially after she was imprisoned.

Emmeline attended a prim lady-like school in Manchester and, when she was fifteen, an even more efficient one in Paris. Three years later she returned to Manchester and helped with her mother's reform work. In 1879, when she was twenty-one, Emmeline married a lawyer who was a keen ally of her mother's, a passionate supporter of women's suffrage. Richard

Marsden Pankhurst, a barrister, was much older than Emmeline but they were happy together and had five children, two sons and three daughters. One son died but Christabel, her eldest child, was to become her close partner in the suffrage campaign that she mounted from her home. The Pankhurst household regularly hosted meetings for many radical people of the time, people like Keir Hardie, Mrs Besant, Sir Charles Dilke and William Morris. When Mr Gladstone refused to include votes for women in his reforms, these people joined the radical Fabian Society.

Dr Pankhurst died in 1898 and Emmeline became Registrar of Births and Deaths in Rusholme, continuing until 1907 when she felt that her increasing commitment to the suffragette movement must have more of her time. In 1903 her group became known as the Women's Social and Political Union and worked quietly but firmly until 1908 when Emmeline and her associates learned a valuable lesson.

They attended an election meeting held by the Liberal candidate, Sir Edward Grey, and questions were asked about women's suffrage. The answers were unsatisfactory and Emmeline and her friends created something of a disturbance which led to them being thrown out of the Free Trade Hall.

They carried on their protests and disturbances in the street and were arrested. This incident hit the headlines in the newspapers and Emmeline learned the value of publicity – good or bad. So began a time of intense activity: disturbances, interrupted meetings, deputations to the House of Commons, women chaining themselves to the railings outside the homes of cabinet ministers, flag waving, and marches. This led to arrests and imprisonment.

That year Emmeline Pankhurst was arrested and placed on a charge of "conduct likely to cause a breach of the peace". Skilfully, she led her own defence, but she was imprisoned for

three months in Holloway. The campaign was intensified in 1909: windows were broken, houses burned and, tragically, one lady threw herself under the hooves of a race horse. Emmeline needed a rest from all of this and so she visited the United States of America later that year.

In 1910 an all party committee recommended that all men should have the vote, but not women. This led to a further escalation of the violence and, in 1912, police raided the headquarters of the Women's Social and Political Union, arresting Mrs Pankhurst and some colleagues. They were tried and convicted on charges of "conspiracy" and imprisoned once more. In protest, the women went on a hunger strike which frightened the authorities so much that they released them.

"Incitement to violence" was the charge in 1913 and imprisonment followed once more. This time the authorities had an answer to the situation when Emmeline went on hunger strike; they released her, but had her re-arrested when she was well again. During the next twelve months she served thirty days of her prison sentence, but at a dreadful cost to her health.

During the four years of the First World War, Emmeline and thousands of other women worked in the factories and this led to a great change in the way the woman's role was viewed.

After the war Emmeline and Christabel Pankhurst went to live in Canada. Christabel married and stayed there, and Emmeline spoke publicly on health and hygiene, until the lure of the Suffragette movement brought her back to England in 1926.

Then, at the age of sixty-eight, she was adopted as Conservative candidate for Whitechapel and St George's and worked devotedly for the people there. Her health was failing fast though, and who can wonder, after her life of struggle and hardship. She died in London on 14th June 1928, but her life's work had not been in vain. Just before she died the People's Act was passed by Parliament, which gave universal suffrage. Success at last!

THE SHADOW OVER BARCROFT HALL

Just beyond Clitheroe lies the village of Walk Mill, and just past the village is Barcroft Hall. Alone on the hillside it sits, grey, shadowy and seemingly full of secrets. Barcroft Hall hid one particular dreadful secret for a lifetime – or, you could say, for two lifetimes.

Thomas Barcroft walked up the hill on March 10th, 1641, and away from the grey hall where he lived. He was full of despair and his feelings seemed to be mirrored in the house he had just left. It had high black windows which looked empty and hollow eyed: seeing nothing, caring about no-one, like Thomas on this day.

With shoulders stooped and feet dragging on the short cropped turf, Thomas climbed the gradual slope towards the summit. He loved to climb the hill usually, as it took him to the fresh air and loneliness, away from his father and mad brother William. Thomas could never please the embittered old man, a widower now for many years, who had never recovered from the horror of having a mentally deranged elder son and heir.

"Heir!" stamped Thomas, suddenly kicking the tussocks of grass. "Heir!" he shouted to the grey skies, his young tortured face creasing in an agony of absolute frustration. His old father was now still in death – never would his whining cry upset and anger his second son again. But the mad giggling and demented wimpering of his brother William would haunt even his deepest sleep for ever more.

Thomas longed to be master of the broad fair acres belonging to Barcroft Hall, but instead of being rested by gazing out over the beautiful countryside, he was sickened by the knowledge that it all belonged to his crazy brother. Thomas tried to look out over the landscape but his eyes could travel no further than the base of the hill where the hall lay. Even now, William would be either crying in the milk sop of his breakfast, watched by old Maggie the housekeeper, or giggling behind Susan, who kept the kitchen and bedrooms tidy. Thomas almost retched with the injustice of his destiny, failing to realise that he could make a pleasant life for himself if he so wished. But no, the devil was in him, capturing his soul, using the evil desires of greed, selfishness and covetousness. So, instead of gazing over the pleasant green land, he glared down at the hall and put together an evil plan that would damn his soul forever.

Hard lines etched his face as Thomas came down the hill to the house with unfaltering strides. His hair streamed backwards and his eyes were bright with the hardness of burnished steel. The great front door banged open and stayed ajar as he entered, stalking through to the kitchen without pause, William looked up, blubbering, from the kitchen table, and old Maggie stood behind him, cooing, and trying to allay his fears. Susan stood wide-eyed and still.

"Get out of the house, the both o' ye," Thomas cried in a strident, high-pitched voice, which did not invite a reply.

Old Maggie, even so, dared to protest, "But, sir, ..."

"Out, out, out!" roared Thomas. And out they scuttled, to go to their rooms and pack their few belongings.

Glowering from the window an hour later, Thomas saw them go up the roadway, glad to be out of the house, though anxious about losing their jobs.

As soon as they had disappeared through the gates, Thomas turned to face his slavering, wide-eyed brother. Even that poor demented soul could sense that something was amiss. Thomas turned, and slowly lit the great candle in the tall brass candlestick. Giving himself no time to soften the hard resolve in his iron heart, Thomas grabbed William and pushed him out of the kitchen and into the passage-way. A door, black and little used, was on the left and Thomas flung it open. Into the darkness a flight of steps sunk downwards and, as the brothers descended, grotesque, flickering shadows fluttered on the walls. William whimpered with fear, but Thomas hustled him downwards, then over the cold brick-paved floor. Chains were hanging from the walls in this room and, as Thomas fastened William to them and secured his bonds, there was a silence between the two brothers: a most awful breathless silence it was.

"Stay ye there, ye daft'un," said Thomas, unable to bear the silence a moment longer. "Ye'll not come twixt me and this land." And, with no further sound, he walked away with the candle, leaving poor William, still silently expectant, chained up there.

William stayed silent, quiet and still for some time in the darkness, waiting for his brother's return. Then he took from his pocket a pencil and scribbled on the wall, giggling with pleasure at the meaning he ascribed to these useless marks.

Slowly, painfully but awfully silently, William died of starvation in that room. Thomas found his body three weeks later and took it outside to dispose of it in the garden.

The Barcroft family name died with the death of Thomas in 1688, for he died wifeless, without an heir, and alone, afraid to share the dreadful secret that he carried. But the lives of Thomas and William Barcroft did not end without trace.

William left his marks on the wall in that room, which can still be seen to this day but, each March 10th, the spirits of the brothers, together, re-enact the events of that evening all those years ago. The passageway is dark, so is the room with the

chains; dark that is, apart from the light from the eyes of a madman and a murderer.

THE BLACK LAD

Ashton-under-Lyne is just another Lancashire town to emerge from nineteenth century industrialisation into the commerce of the twentieth. There is a spacious open market hall and imposing merchants' houses. The restored church of St Michael is noteworthy for its stained glass dating back to about the year 1500. This glass portrays the Asheton family, of whom there is more to tell.

Sir Ralph de Asheton, dressed in a heavy, clanking suit of black armour, emerged from the shadows of the doorway of his manor house at Middleton. Far from handsome, his straggling beard, red-veined cheeks, warted nose and glittering eyes reduced the nobility of his armour to sheer swagger as he strode out to his horse. A stable lad helped him to mount the great black stallion whose lively feet tripped on the hard packed earth of the stable yard. Waiting for him there were seven hard men, clad in leather jerkins, hose and helmets, each astride a fine chestnut horse. Armed with thick black cudgels, they looked, and were, a hard and cruel bunch of men. The grey-stoned manor house and outbuildings, built around a courtyard, were bathed in a soft warm early Spring sunshine, quite inappropriate for the evil gathering. The horses jittered and whinnied anxiously before Sir Ralph cried a curt "Come men, let's away", and off they cantered along the lane that led from the manor house. From the eaved windows, eyes watched, thankful to see the men leave.

It was not always thus with the family who had extremely brave forebears, Robert Bruce, King of Scotland, was defeated at Neville's Cross, near Dunblane, on the 17th October 1346 and an Asheton played his part. It was Thomas Asheton who had borne away the Royal Standard at that battle. For this noble deed, which had fired the courage of the English armies, King

Edward III knighted Thomas as Sir Thomas Asheton of Ashton-under-Lyne. Much later, Sir Ralph's grandson further ennobled the family's name for his prowess in the Battle of Flodden Field. On the 9th of September 1513 he is said to have gone into battle and emerged bringing with him the King of Scotland's standard bearer's sword. Henry VIII was the king to hand out the reward in this instance.

But to return to the dark browed Sir Ralph, who had done nothing to merit his nobility and much to dishonour his title. On this Easter Monday in 1468, just as he had done each year, he was going forth on a spiteful errand which would have been petty, but for its dire consequences.

Over the hill, the little cottages and fields of Ashton-under-Lyne came into view and the landlord, Sir Ralph, slapped his saddle bags and cackled harshly in venomous delight. His henchmen, too, spurred their horses on and they rode into the village, a black group of men oozing evil intent.

The poor people who lived there gathered around their cottages or in the corners of their fields in pitiful groups, casting anxious eyes around them. They looked at their fields and gardens where the crops grew in carefully tended rows. Chickens cackled in their yards, ducks quacked on the pond, cattle lowed in their byres and sheep bleated in their folds. Geese honked on the pastureland and pigs grunted in their styes. But there was no contentment: far from it.

Sir Ralph, with ill-concealed malevolence, jumped from his horse at the first cottage and strode round to the back of it. He upturned an old plank and found some nettles growing there. "Six pence," he called, and strode down the garden and poked among the crops growing in neat rows. "Three pence for a dandelion," he yelled. His henchmen stood by the cottage and, when Sir Ralph emerged again, the man of the house was dropping coins carefully into the huge saddlebag hanging from

Sir Ralph's horse.

They went to the next cottage where more weeds were found in the corner by the fence. "Five pence for these," cried Sir Ralph, and then went on to a patch of ground where the children of the house played. "Ten pence for wasted land," he leered. When the lady of the house sobbed and implored him not to be so hard, Sir Ralph landed his riding crop on her back, laughing as he did so.

When old Jonas and his aged wife could not pay the eight

pence fine for six weeds found in his small garden, Sir Ralph ordered his henchmen to punish them. The cruel men smashed down the cottage door with their clubs and overturned the furniture they found inside. One man went down to the end of the garden and set fire to the pig sty there. Old Jonas followed him howling with fear and tried to set the pig free. The burning rush roof fell off on top of Jonas and his cries of rage and then of pain soon ended in the crackling of the flames. Not in the least disturbed, Sir Ralph carried on with his inspection of his properties with the subsequent fines and punishment for those who could not pay.

Before the sun had sunk beneath the grey dusk's horizon, Sir Ralph, his men and all the coins they had collected, had gone over the hill once more; into the sunset and back to Middleton manor house.

It had been another 'Black Monday', as it was fairly called. Many, many Easter Mondays were passed in this way, often with tragic results, thus justifying that name which all around associated with Ashton-under-Lyne.

When Sir Ralph de Asheton died, the annual custom grew up of taking an effigy of a knight in black armour, called the 'Black Lad', on horseback around the town. It was taken off the horse at the market cross and ritually destroyed by pelting it with stones and rubbish.

It took many years for the hate to subside. The 'Black Lad' custom did not die until about 1960 – the decade known for its 'flower power' and 'love-ins'. So the hatred finally died more than five hundred years later, but the rhyme lives on:

"Sweet Jesu for Thy mercy's sake,
And by Thy bitter passion,
O save me from the burning stake,
And from Sir Ralph de Assheton."

THE BOGGART OF LONGRIDGE

The lanes around Longridge are green and leafy. Surely no evil could exist there? They are a right bonny lot of folk around Longridge, always laughing. And yet men have had their hair turn grey with alarm and women have had theirs turn white with fear.

Tales are told around Longridge of a spirit that comes to terrify the young and lovely. Both men and women are open to this wicked ghost who attacks in the most frightful way – always the same.

Many people, whilst walking along a particular lonely road, have reported seeing an old lady in front of them. She hobbles along, wearing a long coat, an old fashioned bonnet and carrying a basket covered with a cloth. Inevitably, as she is caught up, the old lady will walk alongside, listening to the conversation if there is more than one person there. Just as the walkers are totally deluded by that old lady, she suddenly turns her head to reveal .... an empty bonnet! As the walkers recoil in horror, the old lady snatches the cloth from the basket. Her head, cackling with laughter, falls from the basket to the ground. It bounces along like a grotesque football, following the horrified walker who is now running away with all haste. The awful laughter is afterwards heard ..... in dreams from which the haunted ones awake in a cold sweat.

Many years ago, in a large house in Longridge, there lived a young lady, Alice Dorman, who was the apple of her mother's eye and the peach of her father's. She was an only child and probably thoroughly spoiled, always having the finest and the prettiest of clothes. Alice would pick and choose with her food and even chose her own bedtimes. All in all she grew up to be a very selfish young lady, only intent on pleasing herself. Her mother and father quite despaired of her, but at least she had two redeeming features: her beauty and her sense of humour. Miss Dorman had an elegant form, balanced and perfect in every way. Neat little hands, trim little feet but, due to the clothing worn in those days, an occasional flash of her ankle was all that was ever seen. Long dark brown hair surrounded her angelic face, with its soft ruby lips, smooth pink cheeks and a pair of twinkling deep brown eyes. She rarely used a mirror but she knew of her beauty and used it unashamedly.

Teasing men with her beauty was one of her chief delights. She would make her eyes sparkle, her lips smile and her whole body speak as she followed some young man, just to make him fancy that romance had come his way. Just as he tried to respond to Alice's advances, she would pout and turn her nose up, generally giving the impression that he was not good enough.

"Chasing after men like that, my girl," her mother would say. "What on earth are you thinking of?"

"But it's only a game, mother," Alice would reply.

"Yes, and it's a game that will end in you a'chasing people and never catching them, Alice. It's a game that will have a wicked end."

Alice's sense of humour was often to the fore. She loved to play tricks on her unfortunate friends and acquaintances. Much to the shame of her mother, she would sometimes walk with a limp. When friends enquired of the cause of the limp, she would make up the most awful of stories: a dog had bitten her; she had caught her foot in a rabbit trap; someone had shot at her. The more they sympathised, the more sorry for herself she became and almost believed her own stories. At other times she would put her arm in the sleeve of her coat, and again dreadful fibs were told: her finger had been poisoned; she had had an accident with an axe; had caught her hand in a milk churn.

Her mother wrung her hands in despair. "You just wait, young lady. Someday someone will play a joke on you." At other times she would cry, "One of these days the wind will change and you'll stay like it."

Never for a moment did Alice's mother think that these things were possibilities, but what if they were? Could something like that happen?

One day Alice Dorman thought of her most awful trick ever. She hunched a great black coat up so that the collar was buttoned up, but buttoned up OVER the top of her head. Then on top of the collar Alice balanced a pig's bladder which the housekeeper's boy had blown up and used to kick around. On this bladder was cunningly painted a face – a most realistic looking face.

Down the road near the Dorman house in the village of Longridge came a carriage carrying a young gentleman, Rodney Faversham. He had fond hopes of courting Alice for he was very attracted by the sparkle in her eyes. As the carriage progressed, young Rodney saw a tall young lady walking down the road towards him. Suddenly the young lady appeared to trip, and the watching Rodney saw her head fall off and go bouncing down the road! Gallant and brave he might have been, but he quite fainted away. The horseman driving the carriage was so startled that his mouth hung open and he relaxed his hold on the reins. The horses sensed his fears, neighed wildly, and reared up on their back legs with their forefeet flailing in the air. Suddenly they lunged forward in a breakaway gallop, wild and careless. Sadly, they crashed into our dear Alice, who was bent double at the discomfiture of poor Rodney.

Alice died instantly, her skull quite broke: she had passed away

laughing her head off!

But that careless laughter is still heard today in the lovely but lonely lanes around Longridge. Along one road in particular she still plays the same trick on passers by. Hers is a bad but harmless spirit, destined to play her silly joke forever.

JAMES HARGREAVES

The great mills, which brought such wealth to the hills and dales of Lancashire, owed their prosperity to the pioneer inventors, Arkwright, Hargreaves, Cartwright, Crompton and Jacquard. Their lives are all worthy of research and study, none more so than James Hargreaves, whose story is told here.

James Hargreaves was born in Standhill, a little village just outside Blackburn, in 1745. He and his brothers and sisters were practically born with the sound of the loom in their ears, because their mother and father were both spinners and weavers of wool. The little cottage where he was born was demolished many years ago and, indeed, the world as he knew it has disappeared too.

In the middle of the 18th Century, parts of Lancashire were already quite industrialised. Coalmines had been there for many years, but by this time there were many small factories where people gathered together to work at the production of cloth. Usually it was wool, but the cotton industry of Lancashire was to grow on the back of the woollen industry which already thrived. Although the factories were there, the streams that ran down the hillsides were clear and clean, the trees and meadows flourished green and verdant, and the skies were clear.

Into the port of Liverpool started to come the raw cotton. From there it went to the small factories and to the cottages, where men and women wove it using the old spinning wheels and looms. The demand for cloth, both cotton and wool, was great and the search started for improved ways of spinning and weaving. This was the world of young James Hargreaves.

James and his two brothers and young sister played on the floor near their mother, as her spinning wheel whispered the afternoon away. An elder brother helped their father as he worked the shuttle on the loom at the far end of the cottage. Up and down the row of houses there was this pattern of the mother and father working, tending the children too small for work and teaching those old enough the ways of the wheel and the loom. James tired of playing with the others and sat close to his mother's knee, fascinated by the turning of the wheel, the growth of the wool on the bobbin and the steady beat of his mother's foot. The sun beat through the open doorway and James dozed, leaning heavily against his mother. Although she was tired, she let young James stay where he was. "You'll soon be into work, James lad, so sleep on whilst you can."

There was no school for James, or the other children like him who lived in Standhill, for work was all they were ever likely to know. Spinning and weaving were the only skills they needed, so why waste time teaching them to read, write and do arithmetic?

James spent long hours watching, then learning, and eventually working, either in his parent's cottage or in the factory at Blackburn which was owned by Sir Robert Peel's grandfather. He married a neighbour, Jenny, and set up his own little house, complete with its spinning wheel and loom. James and Jenny hoped that soon they would add children too.

One day, whilst James was waiting for his wife to finish a bobbin of weft thread on her spinning wheel, he accidentally knocked her primitive wheel over. As it lay on the floor, the wheel continued to turn and the bobbins to spin. Suddenly it struck him that a wheel spinning horizontally could power several upright bobbins, and therefore spin several threads simultaneously. He spent the next few months using all his scant leisure time in experimentation and eventually made a

machine that would spin eight or twelve threads at a time. He called this his 'spinning jenny', after his wife, and was very happy with his success. He made a few for neighbours too, so they could earn more money. This was his big mistake.

People started to talk and to say that James Hargreaves was meddling with machinery which would put eleven out of twelve of them out of work, that the countryside would become depopulated and they would finish up unable to earn a living. A meeting of spinners and weavers was held and the gathering decided to go straight to James's cottage to deal with the matter. Fortunately the family were out but his machine was smashed to pieces, and those he had made for his neighbours.

They then marched to Peel's Mill where James worked and completely demolished the place.

James Hargreaves was shocked by the ill feeling and violence and moved to Nottingham where he met up with a thrifty carpenter named Thomas James. Thomas was very interested to hear about the 'spinning jenny' and realised that he could use the money he had saved, and make much more besides, by going into partnership with James. In 1770 a patent was obtained for the machine and James Hargreaves and Thomas James seemed well set up.

However, the mill-owners of Blackburn were quick to see the advantages of the spinning jenny and, notwithstanding the patent, they set about pirating the idea and making their own versions. This gave the cotton industry a tremendous boost, increasing production greatly.

When James Hargreaves saw what was happening, he decided to prosecute the mill owners for stealing his invention. The mill owners formed an association against him and employed some very famous lawyers. When James' solicitor became aware of the number and the wealth of the opposition, he threw in his brief and advised James to give in. It was totally unjust, but James followed his lawyer's recommendation.

Not everyone was dishonest, though, so James and his partner continued to produce and sell their spinning jennies. When he died in 1778 James was worth some six or seven thousand pounds, although it is said that his children afterwards fell into great poverty.

The house James and Jenny Hargreaves lived in is now Standhill Post Office and there is a tablet on the wall which tells the story of James and the invention of his spinning jenny. It was seeing this tablet that started my search for this story.

THE WHITE DOE

Cliviger Gorge is near Burnley, outside Towneley. It is an ancient and fascinating place, full of romance and history. Towneley Hall is open to the public and well worth a visit. Go there and then visit Eagle Crag, as hard-bitten, windswept and deserted a place as you could imagine. Feel the poignant mystery there. Spirits of another age seem to accompany visitors as they look over the steep edge.

It was here, at Eagle Crag, that Sir William Towneley buried his wife in sad and very tender circumstances. Sir William dearly loved his wife, Lady Sybil, and it broke his heart when she died.

The country was very unsettled in the early Tudor times when William was a boy. It was the 1490's and he and his family lived in the hunting lodge at Towneley and Sir John, William's father, was often away at the court of King Henry VII. There were plans laid in those days to turn their lodge into a fine mansion but, because of the unrest, this did not happen quickly. The job was eventually completed by a nephew of Sir William.

The Towneleys were very well thought of locally because they were good landlords and masters. They were welcome guests wherever they called and kind hosts when they in turn were visited.

Young William and his pony wandered far and wide, alone but safe, getting to know the hills and valleys, the plants, animals and birds of the moors very well indeed.

In the Spring of 1496 the heather on the moors seemed bejewelled with flowers, the birds chorused their delightful

songs and William fell in love. It was Easter Monday and the Towneleys were visiting Gawthorpe Hall when William saw Sybil for the first time. As they rode down the avenue of dark trees, they saw the Hall, glimmering in the sunshine in front of them and Sybil was standing by the door. She was just seventeen and very beautiful, a real golden girl: William was bewitched. An evening of feasting and entertainment followed a happy day and often, with the minstrels singing and playing in the background, William and Sybil's eyes met. The bond was formed. As the wine flowed, William eventually moved towards Sybil and very shyly spoke to her.

"May I see you, one day soon, so that we can talk?" he asked.

"I have many things to do," Sybil replied, rather surprisingly, although she smiled kindly.

"But could you not find time for us to get to know each other?" urged William. "I am sure that your family would not be against it."

"Oh, I am certain that they would not, but I have very little spare time," answered Sybil, and William had to accept that for the moment.

But William was not satisfied. Every day he rode to Gawthorpe and saw Sybil striding over the moors. Whenever he tried to follow, her tracks were lost to him amongst the bushes and scrub. On each occasion, though, William noticed a large, white doe on the moors and often saw a small, white cat near Gawthorpe Hall. Was this just a coincidence? His love for Sybil was magnified by her rejection of him, and his yearning to be with her increased.

Throughout the summer William looked for, and lived for Sybil, but to no avail. In desperation, he sought the advice of Old Betty Shawcote and, in the smoke-filled room of her hovel down by the river, told her his woeful tale. When he mentioned his sightings of the doe and the cat, Old Betty cackled loudly.

"Why, young man, don't 'ee know? Thems is your Sybil! She's a witch – and a good 'en too. 'Tis said she's a lost soul. Sold 'er soul .... to the Devil!"

"No, no, Betty, no! I want her for my wife. Please help me," pleaded William.

"If 'er soul's to be saved there is only one chance," continued Old Betty. "Now, you listen carefully and do as I say."

William did listen carefully and did exactly as she said. On All Hallows Day, that is the first day of November, he went hunting the white doe on Eagle Crag and in his hand he carried the enchanted silken rope that he had been given by Old Betty. He was accompanied by a hound, also provided by Old Betty because it had magical powers. Together they trapped the doe

in some bushes and then tied up the creature with the silken thread. Immediately the white doe changed back into the form of the seventeen year old girl.

Sybil was desperately afraid because she had been unmasked, but William poured out his feelings of love for her and she agreed to become his wife. There was another agreement too: no more dabbling with magic and the black arts.

Sir William and Lady Sybil were married in Gawthorpe Church and they settled down to live in Towneley. The plans to enlarge the hunting lodge were revitalised as the young couple also planned on having a family.

All was happiness for a while, but after a few months the call of Satan came to Lady Sybil and she went back to her old habits of roaming the countryside as a white doe or cat.

It was while she was playing on the wheel of Cliviger Mill, in the guise of a white cat, that she caught her paw in the turning wheel. Blood dripped from the cat's leg as it leaped from the mill and, on three legs, crawled off into the undergrowth.

Lady Sybil arrived back at Towneley Lodge with her hand torn off. She would not tell Sir William what had happened as she had grown to love him very much. She did not want to admit that she had gone back to her magic and sometimes evil ways. Unable to bear the truth of her disloyalty, Lady Sybil wasted away into death and Sir William, suspecting something of what had happened, buried her in an unmarked grave by Eagle Crag in Cliviger Gorge.

And ever since, at dusk on Hallowe'en, Eagle Crag has been haunted by the restless spirits of the doe, the hound and the huntsman. As the countryside loses its colour on the fateful night of the year, the evil spirits are abroad. 'Tis best to stay at home.

LOST TO A MERMAID

**If you took the underground train from
Liverpool to New Brighton then walked to the
seafront you would be able to see the Black
Rock. It is covered by a fort now, but dream
your way back to a day of sand and sunshine in
the early seventeen-hundreds and lose
yourself once more into the wonderland of folk
legend.**

The wharf at the Liverpool docks was a whirl of noise, dust,
movement and life and Joe Drake was anxious to be away
from it all. He had arrived from India the day before in a tall
ship, bringing a cargo of tea, spices, hemp and fine wood. The
holds of the sleek wooden vessel had been packed with goods
of great value and its crew had been paid well for what had
been a calm and peaceful voyage. Now the sailors had a week
to spend in port and most had gone to their homes and the
arms of their waiting families. In contrast, Joe felt lonely and
forlorn because he was an orphan, alone in the world and with
no home to go to.

He stood in the shadow of a great warehouse and watched the
cargoes being unloaded from his ship, the Persephone, and the
other ships which stood by. It was a fine sight. Straining horses
pulling great wagons left the ships' sides, their waggoners
urging them on. The more they carried the greater was their
pay but in their haste an occasional bale of cotton or package
of spices fell to the ground, bursting on impact. Immediately,
one of the watching foremen would rush to the place so that
the goods did not get 'lost' into a different wagon or under a
waggoner's cloak, to be sold on the side later. Tally men stood
with their sticks and boards and the occasional ship-owner
stood watching proudly. The neighing of tired horses, the
shouting of the men as they encouraged the horses, the calling

of the dockers and the mewing of the gulls mingled with the washing sea sounds, the grinding of the wheels on the stones of the wharf and the squeaking of the axles. These noises were a wild accompaniment to the turning of the wheels, the swaying of the masts, the flashing hooves and the running and rushing of the men. This was a whirligig to Joe after his long peaceful voyage and he longed to escape. Off he walked, towards the loneliness and quietness of the countryside, beyond the bustle of the port.

As the houses petered out, he entered the scrub and wilderness of the foreland. Only the occasional cottage was to be seen along the road and although Joe was alone he was not lonely. The emptiness of the landscape exactly matched his solitary mood.

Joe reached the shore at low tide in the early afternoon, the heat of the June sunshine hot on his back and head. The low water allowed him to walk out to the Black Rock island and he flopped down on the warm sand, worn out by the effort of the trek which had dispelled his frustration. Almost instantly he fell into a dreamless sleep, his tanned face quite calm and his curly head nestling on his hands in the sand.

What it was that awakened Joe we do not know; it could have been a cool breeze or the lost cry of a seagull. Whatever it was, his eyelids fluttered momentarily, then he sat bolt upright. The waves washed the shore gently, the causeway to the beach now lost beneath the waters of the tide. As Joe's eyes took in the scene he saw the beautiful face of a long-haired girl playing in the waves. "Hi!" he called, hoping that she would answer. But when she saw Joe she looked surprised and vanished beneath the waves. Joe stood up, concerned when she did not surface, and started to wade into the water. "Hello there!" he cried out. And there, over there, some yards from the beach, the head appeared again. "Don't be afraid lass," Joe called. This time the head stayed above the water, a soft smile playing on her lips and in her eyes. Joe continued to wade out until he was within a few feet of her. He saw the beautiful form of a young lady in the waters and the absolutely perfect face of the girl of his dreams.

"Hello," she said, her husky voice like pearls from deep sea shells.

"I'm Joe, lass, and what are you called?"

"Come," she replied, swimming to the shore.

Joe gasped with amazement as she climbed from the clinging sea to recline on a rock in the sun for, perfect young lady from the waist upwards she may have been but, from the waist downwards she had the silver tail of a fish!

Quite unperturbed, she began: "My name is Caroline and my

family was lost in a shipwreck many years ago ....." And she told him a wondrous story of how her whole family, now living with lost souls beneath the sea, had perished in a shipwreck tragedy. Recently she had become separated from her family in a storm and she had surfaced whilst searching for them.

Joe held her hand, quite entranced by both her appearance and her tale. He told her of his lonely life, at sea and on shore, and her lustrous eyes gazed upon him with love and fascination. The sun was sinking fast in the west as their conversation drew to a close and the mermaid said that she must go on to continue her search. Looking at him and smiling her goodbyes, Caroline dropped from the rock and into the sea. Joe looked at the spot and out to sea for ages, hoping for her return.

When it grew dark he waded waist deep through the sea, back to the shore, and started the long walk back to his lodgings in

Liverpool. The following morning Joe went to a jeweller in the city and bought the finest gold ring in the shop. Afterwards he retraced his steps of the day before, through the busy streets, the open countryside, and back to the Black Rock. It was another golden sunshiny day, full of all the colours of the rainbow, but Joe was lost in his loving thoughts of Caroline.

Back at the island, he lay on the sand again and looked out to sea, hoping and praying for sight of that lovely face and long fair hair. The sun made him drowsy and he fell asleep, the ring he had bought that morning firmly clutched in his hand.

Once more Joe awoke with a start, feeling her presence immediately. Sure enough, there in the blue wavelets was Caroline. She swam to the shore and perched herself on the rock and, there in the sunshine, they talked again and vowed their love for each other. Gently she led him into the sea. Joe was afraid at first then, gaining confidence as she led him into the deeper water, went willingly with her, his brown eyes as much led by her bright blue ones as by her strong white hands. In gentle tones she told him of the everlasting life beneath the waters and of the family she had found again.

"Come with me, Joe. I will be lonely without you," she said. Joe, losing his soul to her beguiling words and alluring eyes, followed her without question, dipping his head beneath the waters as she dived.

Some fishermen, landing on Black Rock later that day, came across the body of a young seaman who had a beautiful smile upon his clear, young face. They searched for a sign of his identity but nothing could be found. Strangely, there was no trace of the ring which he had bought. But how could there be? It was on the third finger of a mermaid, Caroline, who dances forever behind the waves, just off the Black Rock, laughing gently in the foam, hand in hand with the soul of that lost sailor?